Face Ache

by TOM ARMSTRONG

RAVETTE PUBLISHING

First Published by
Ravette Publishing Limited 1997

Printed and bound for
Ravette Publishing Limited,
Unit 3, Tristar Centre
Star Road, Partridge Green
West Sussex RH13 8RA

by Proost, Belgium

ISBN: 1 85304 935 2

SIMPLY IRRESISTIBLE!

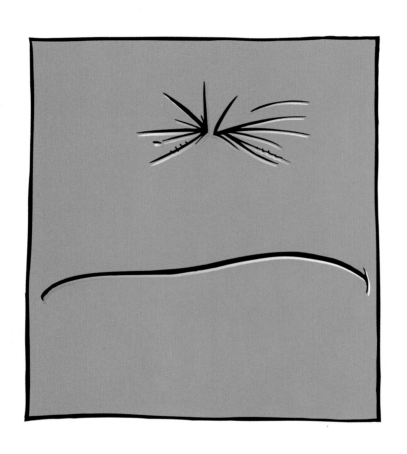

WAKE ME WHEN IT'S THE
WEEKEND...

STRESSED OUT!!!

I DON'T THINK SO!!

FREAK OUT !!!!

WHAT HORMONES?!!

GET OUT OF MY FACE!

TOTALLY BUMMED

NO BRAINER

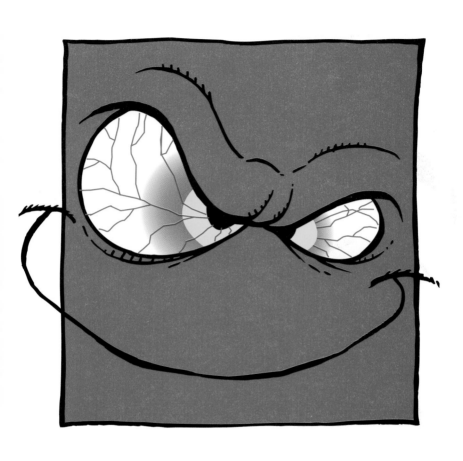

DON'T GET MAD, GET EVEN!

WAY COOL

CAFFEINE HIGH!!

UNPLUGGED

JUST KIDDING!

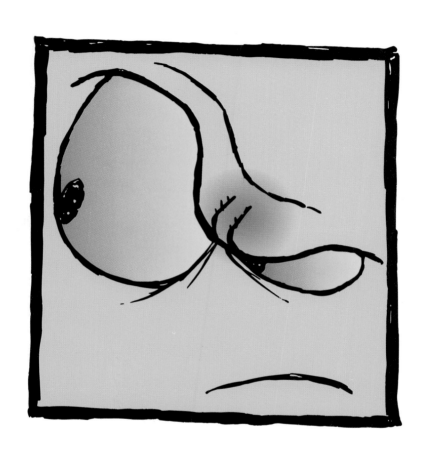

LOOK, BUT DON'T TOUCH

GOOD AT BEING BAD!

I AM A WOMAN,
HEAR ME ROAR!

BOOOOOORING

ADORABLY CUTE!

LOOKING FOR LOVE

IT WASN'T ME

WHATEVER

WHAT ARE YOU
LOOKING AT?!

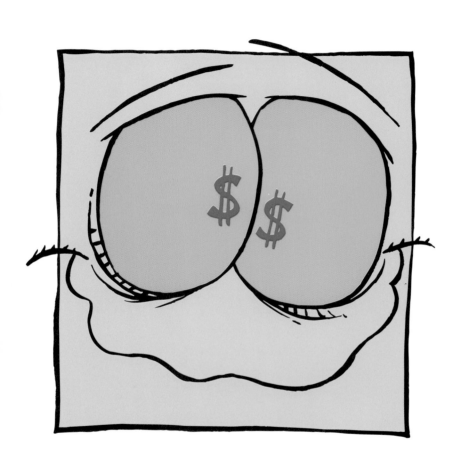

MALL MANIAC!

'CAUSE I SAID SO!!

TEED OFF!!!

REEL MAN

LOOKIN' GOOD, GIRL!

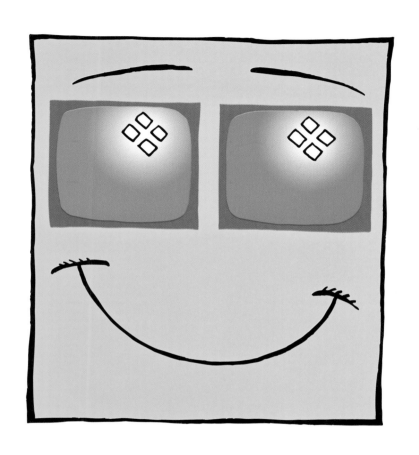

RULER OF THE REMOTE

FATHER OF A TEENAGER!!

SHAKEN, NOT STIRRED

WHO ARE YOU CALLING
"OLD MAN"?!

MR. <u>UN</u> FIX IT!

FATHER IN THE 'HOOD

DADITUDE

BITE ME !!

WHY ME ?

A STAR IS BORN

SAVE THE LECTURE

MEGAGIFTED

ANGEL

DON'T GO THERE

YEAH, RIGHT!

SO CONFUSED

WHAT PART OF "NO" DON'T YOU UNDERSTAND?

COMPLETELY MENTAL!!

COMPLETELY
UNDERWHELMED

CAUTION:
DANGEROUS CURVES

'CAUSE I SAID SO!!

HAVE YOUR PEOPLE
CALL MY PEOPLE

MISSED MY NAP!

TRUE ROMANTIC

BAD IF I WANNA BE!

SPOILED BRAT

KISS ME ! !

REBEL

JUST WANNA
HAVE FUN

STRESSED OUT

FLIRT

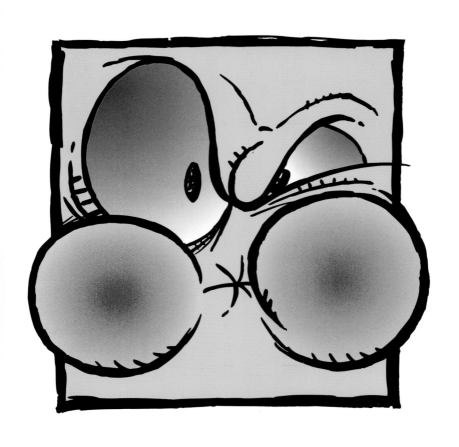

SUCK IT UP

BUH-URR-RRPP!!